Judy Allen has won the Whitbread Award and the Friends of the Earth Earthworm Award. She is the author of more than fifty books, and she also writes for radio.

Of this book, Judy Allen says, ' I really enjoyed working on it because the more I learned about John Snow, the more I respected and liked him. Also, reading about his work on cholera was a bit like reading a mystery story in which a horrific villain is relentlessly tracked down by a doggedly determined detective.'

D0581196

To Beverley, who gave me the idea

Contents

The Miasma of the Past

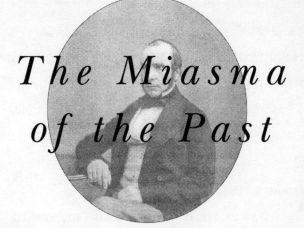

1836, AND A MIASMA HUNG OVER London, made up of the stench from cesspools and abattoirs; from dung and urine and boiling animal bones; from rubbish tips and manufacturing processes.

Often the miasma was visible, stained a greyish-yellow colour by coal and wood smoke. It lifted when a clean wind blew. It sagged down to the muddy streets when the wind dropped. At night it dimmed the gaslights that hissed softly along the main streets.

It was believed to carry disease. It was believed that the seeds of every terrible sickness, including many that were fatal, were caught up in its foetid mist. And certainly it smelt – and even tasted – of illness and putrefaction. It was like some vast, faceless creature that came creeping through the streets when the air was still, sending long, wispy fingers into the alleys as if searching for victims.

The higher parts of the city rose above its murk like islands, but down by the Thames the foggy pall was reluctant to disperse.

The Thames itself – busy with barges and steamboats, watermen, lightermen and scavenging 'river finders' – was almost an open sewer. Flush lavatories were not yet commonplace. Most people used earth closets or privies. The waste went through the drains or else into one of the thousands of cesspools, which leaked their stinking contents into underground streams. And drains and underground streams alike emptied themselves into the river.

The Thames embankments, elegantly designed by Joseph Bazalgette, weren't begun until the 1860s, so the Thames was wider than now and often swilled into the basements of the nearest buildings, taking its horrible cargo with it. The river is tidal as far as Teddington, which meant that sewage was pushed back up the outlets when the water level was high. Also, it was washed upriver and back down again, day after day, to the rhythm of the tides, together with dead dogs, drowned rats and the occasional human body.

And this was the main source of drinking water for the city.

There were several different water companies, but few drew clean water from upriver; most drew supplies from the polluted lower reaches. Even then, not every house had mains water and none had it permanently on tap. The companies would make it available for a couple of hours a day, and never on a Sunday. So it had to be stored, or else collected from a local pump.

Cast-iron pumps, dotted around the streets, brought it to the surface from shallow wells, none more than thirty feet below ground. Some were more popular than others. In Soho, for example, the pump in Carnaby Street was hardly used because the water had such a foul smell.

Oddly, Londoners who were afraid of the miasma were not afraid of the water. Yet they should have been. In less than twenty years, the fact that the water was deadlier than the air would be demonstrated by a Yorkshireman who first arrived in London in the autumn of 1836.

However, London was no worse than any other major city and certainly more exciting than most. It was not all fog and slums. It was an important centre for banking, engineering, shipbuilding and manufacturing, with many beautiful buildings and elegant leafy squares. It was a city full of activity and possibilities, and it drew people towards it as powerfully then as it does now.

One of those it attracted was John Snow, who travelled to the capital from his home in York where he had lived with his parents and his five younger brothers and three younger sisters.

He walked all the way.

It would be another ten years until there was a rail link between the two cities. There were stagecoaches, but journeys made on foot were far more common then than now. Also, John Snow was twenty-three years old, very fit, an enthusiastic walker – and he spent the whole summer on the trek.

There's no record of the route he followed, though it is certain he walked first to Liverpool, which meant crossing the Pennines. From there he made his way south through Wales. Even if he avoided the highest mountains he would have had many steep climbs through the Welsh hills. He must have crossed the River Severn somewhere, possibly by the old stone bridge at Gloucester, and he definitely stayed for a while in Bath with his mother's brother Charles Empson. The two were good friends, as well as uncle and nephew, and remained so for the rest of John Snow's life. When at last he left his uncle's house, he took the Bath road to the capital. He wanted to be a doctor, and he was moving to London to study at the Hunterian School of Medicine in Great Windmill Street, Soho.

The route to becoming a fully qualified doctor is different now, but John Snow had followed the usual method of the time, becoming an apprentice when he was fourteen years old. His first apprenticeship was with William Hardcastle who had a practice in Newcastle upon Tyne. Next he assisted a doctor called Watson in Burnop Field, just outside Newcastle. Finally he worked as assistant to Mr Warburton at his practice in Pately Bridge in Yorkshire, now a small town, but then a very remote village.

When he arrived in London, he found lodgings at No. 11 Bateman's Buildings, near Soho Square. He didn't leave a description, but we know 11 Bateman's Buildings was a slightly run-down three-storey house, like many others in London where students and single people of limited means could rent a room. Usually a lodging like this would be run by a couple, possibly with children, or perhaps by a widow. Either way, a maidservant would be employed to clean the lodgers' rooms, light fires, and carry washing water. A lodger like John Snow would most likely eat with the family, and even if he bought his own food it would probably be cooked by the landlady.

The walk from Bateman's Buildings through the

southern part of Soho to the Hunterian School of Medicine was not long – certainly not for a walker like John Snow – but it would have been noisy and smelly.

Soho, in the Parish of St James, Westminster, was extremely overcrowded. Many of the once-smart Georgian terraces had become rookeries, with several families living in each house, often with a whole family to a room. The area was full of activity and noise. As well as living accommodation there were numerous small shops, dining rooms, coffee houses, schools, a brewery, a workhouse with dead-house attached and a factory making percussion caps for rifles.

Also, according to the Honourable Frederick Byng, who wrote a pamphlet about the health hazards of the area, there were "14 cow-sheds, 2 slaughter houses, 3 boiling houses, 7 bone stores ... Two of these sheds are ... within yards of the backs of the houses ... 40 cows are kept in them, each live in seven feet of space. There is no ventilation ... Besides the animals there is, at one end, a large tank for grains, a store place for turnips and hay, and between them a receptacle into which the liquid manure drains, and the solid is heaped."

Probably none of this would have seemed all that extraordinary to the young John Snow. York would have had its own hygiene problems – and if there seemed to be more filth in London it was only because London was bigger and far more over-crowded.

He wouldn't even have been surprised by the amount of illness in the city. Sickness and early death were not uncommon anywhere and although he wasn't yet qualified, he had already had a lot of medical experience, including experience with a horrific disease which was, at that time, new to England. Or perhaps it wasn't totally new, but it certainly took a very new form.

A sickness called cholera – sometimes known as common cholera, English cholera or summer diarrhoea – tended to flare up each autumn. 'Common cholera' was almost certainly a covering name for a whole range of gastric or intestinal disorders which were unpleasant and uncomfortable, but usually only fatal to the very young or those who were already frail.

However, the cholera that appeared for the first time in England in 1831, in the port of Sunderland, was very different.

This disease, which came to be called Asiatic Cholera, had started in India and moved across Asia and Europe at a steady pace, rapidly reaching epidemic proportions in every country it touched. It was almost immeasurably worse than the local form. It could kill the strong as readily as the weak.

It was unstoppable and untreatable, its path was unpredictable, and as no one knew what form the infection took, or how it travelled, there seemed no defence against it.

Asiatic cholera first hit Britain in 1831, and John Snow had encountered it when William Hardcastle sent him to the colliery at Killingworth to try to help the miners who had been stricken with it. The violent and fearful epidemic had died out three years before Snow's arrival in London.

But it would be back.

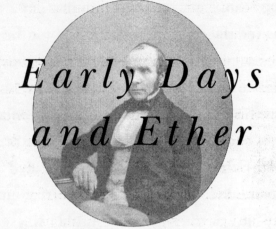

Chapter 2

Early Days and Ether

CHOLERA HAD GONE, FOR THE TIME BEING AT LEAST, but there were plenty of other ills for a doctor to concern himself with. Life expectancy was shorter than it is now, and infant and child mortality were higher. The big killers were pneumonia, smallpox, typhoid and consumption. Children were especially at risk from measles, scarlet fever and whooping cough.

The children of poor families – and poverty was extreme and extensive – very often suffered from rickets, a softening of the bones brought about by malnutrition and also by lack of sunlight. Sunlight was a rare experience to the children of large families, living in one dingy room and spending from eight to twelve hours a day working in a factory or sweatshop.

John Snow had probably encountered most or all of these ills during his apprenticeships, but at this stage his main concern was to study and become a qualified doctor. He enrolled at the Hunterian School of Medicine and attended lectures and demonstrations on chemistry, anatomy and physiology, surgery, medicine and botany.

There were also classes on practical anatomy. This meant dissection. Dead bodies were regularly collected for medical schools so that students could watch their tutors dissect them – and then experiment for themselves.

Unfortunately this added to the general suspicion of doctors and hospitals that was around at the time. Cutting up bodies, even in the cause of science, was seen as gruesome and unfeeling. Also, some people were afraid that the medical men thought studying illness was more important than curing it. But John Snow would have been well aware that there can be no cure without knowledge, and that probing around in a corpse was as important, in its way, as delving into a textbook.

He was a hard worker. When he was involved in dissecting he often stayed on well into the evening rather than stop in the middle of some really interesting piece of research.

Joshua Parsons, a lifelong friend who first met him when they were fellow students at the Hunterian school, left a nice description of him. "Dr Snow was, as a student, characterized by the same mental qualities which have marked him ever since. Not particularly quick of apprehension, or ready in invention, he yet always kept in the foreground by his indomitable perseverance and determination in following up whatever line of investigation was open to him. The object of this steady pursuit with him was always truth: the naked truth, for its own sake, was what he sought and loved."

It's clear that, all his life, John Snow regarded truth as far more important than wealth or honours. It's also clear that he held strong opinions. He would always listen to another point of view, and he would never get cross or argumentative – but he didn't often change his mind.

When he was seventeen he read a book about vegetarianism. It convinced him that meat was an unnecessary and unsuitable food, and he became vegetarian at once. Vegetarianism wasn't very common in Britain at that time, and most of the people he knew thought it was all rather peculiar.

Benjamin Richardson, another close doctor friend, recorded that when Snow lived at Pately Bridge, as apprentice to Dr Warburton, his eating habits "puzzled the housewives, shocked the cooks and astonished the children". Still, the housewives and cooks provided the right food, and John Snow, who always got on very well with children and had a nice sense of humour, probably got them to laugh with him, even if he couldn't persuade them to agree with him. He may even have shown off a bit, to prove how strong his diet made him. Richardson remarks that Snow was an excellent swimmer and "could make headway against the tide longer than any of his omnivorous friends".

Joshua Parsons, who never came round to the idea of meatless meals, wrote "... many and great were the controversies held between us on the subject. These led to trials of our comparative strength and endurance, in one of which, on Easter Monday 1837, we walked to St Alban's, and back to town through Harrow – a distance, I believe, of rather more than fifty miles. On reaching the Edgware Road my companion was fairly beaten, and obliged to reach home in an omnibus. But though this, you will say, shows a fair amount of strength, yet it was my impression that my friend's constitutional powers were impaired by his mode of living..."

About a decade later, Snow was finally persuaded to start eating a little meat again for the sake of his health, but he never lost his belief that "vegetarian practice was commendable, in that it kept the body in better tone for the exercise of the mind."

The vegetarian diet in the 1830s was probably

quite simple – porridge, haricot beans, potatoes, cabbage and a few other vegetables, lentil soup, rough wholemeal bread, and some cheese. It should have been sustaining enough, but the problem may have been that busy cooks, who didn't see the point of it anyway, too often dished out over-cooked vegetables and didn't bother with the beans, cheese and other sources of protein. Still, it was very much in character that John Snow tried out the diet he believed in on himself, just as, later on, he tested medicines on himself before giving them to his patients.

In 1837, having completed his studies at the Hunterian School, he enrolled in the Medical School at Westminster Hospital, and passed the qualifying exam of the Royal College of Surgeons in the May of 1838. This meant he was qualified to practice general medicine. (The doctors now known as General Practitioners, or GPs, were known as Surgeons then.)

In the September of 1837, he moved out of his student lodgings in Bateman's Buildings and rented a house at 54 Frith Street, just around the corner near Soho Square. It belonged to a Mrs Williamson, who was a widow. This time John Snow was the only lodger, which meant he had the whole house to himself, although Mrs Williamson may have stayed on to look after him. Either way, it is more than likely that he would have employed help. A man in his position, lowly though it still was, would be very unlikely to do his own housework, laundry and cooking. In those days servants were not only for the rich. For women, going into domestic service was seen as preferable to factory work or sewing from dawn to night in some sweatshop, so there was a plentiful supply. Also, the wages were extremely low, so even a modest household could employ at least one servant.

In October, John Snow achieved another crucial qualification. He was admitted to the Worshipful Company of Apothecaries. This was essential because it meant he was licensed to prepare and sell medicines. Immediately he set up practice from his Frith Street address. He continued to take courses at the University of London, and became Dr Snow in November 1843 (the year the statue of Lord Nelson was heaved a hundred and forty-five feet into the air and placed on top of the column in Trafalgar Square).

Dr Snow quickly joined the Westminster Medical Society – clearly a good move because he later maintained that all his successes stemmed from his association with it. Despite the fact that he was very shy, and had a husky voice that meant he was not always easy to understand, still he stood up and spoke at meetings – although it was hard going at first. Benjamin Richardson supplies a vivid picture of a closed clique of men deliberately giving a newcomer a hard time. "At first, as he told me, nobody ever replied to what he said." It was a long time before someone deigned to respond to something he said – but even then he simply referred to Snow as 'the last speaker'. However, some time later a member called him by name, and finally someone not only called him by name but actually agreed with what he had said. Eventually, in 1841, he was invited to present his own paper, "Asphyxia and the

Resuscitation of new-born Children", reading it aloud to the assembled members. A breakthrough!

But still his earnings were dismally low. The National Health Service was a long way in the future, but some of the poor belonged to sick clubs, set up and subsidised by various institutions including the Friendly Societies (which were early trades unions) and the church. From the start he worked with hospital patients, and he had four sick clubs attached to his practice, but although all this meant a lot of hard work it provided a very small income indeed.

It was a long time before he managed to attract paying patients.

Benjamin Richardson was sure he knew why. He was certain the problem was that Snow had no contacts, no-one well placed enough to introduce him to rich, bored old ladies who would pay well for a good bedside manner and a bottleful of pills.

He also says that Snow had not "the least element of quackery in all his composition". The quacks (unqualified practitioners who called themselves doctors) often earned their livings with a mixture of charm and jargon. They were unlikely to suggest the patient change his or her life style but would hand out 'remedies' that, at best, did no actual harm. They were very popular with some patients. From the beginning, though, John Snow was more interested in trying to remove the causes of a disease than in simply dishing out medicine. This might be what patients need, but – then as now – it isn't always what they want.

However, Snow's finances began to change for the better in 1846 when the first surgical anaesthetic – ether – became available.

The early use of ether in Britain was not always very successful, but Snow, who was immediately interested in the possibilities, realised that the problem was not so much with the ether itself but with the method of giving it to the patient. He set out to solve the problem by designing a more efficient ether inhaler.

Benjamin Richardson describes a chance meeting between Snow and an acquaintance that turned out to be very significant: "One day, on coming out of one of the hospitals (I am giving the narrative as he gave it to me), he met ... a druggist whom he knew, bustling along with a large ether apparatus under his arm.

'Good morning!' said Dr Snow.

'Good morning to you, doctor!' said the friend, 'but don't detain me, I am giving ether here, there and everywhere, and am getting quite into an ether practice.'

'Rather peculiar,' said the doctor to himself; 'rather peculiar, certainly! For the man has not the remotest chemical or physiological idea on the subject. An ether practice! If he can get an ether practice, perchance some scraps of the same thing might fall to a scientific unfortunate.'"

Encouraged by this meeting, Snow approached St George's Hospital with his new improved inhaler, and was allowed to act as anaesthetist, first for a tooth extraction and then for an operation. Soon he was in charge of giving most of the ether needed in London. In 1847, he produced a detailed book on the subject and early editions sold very well among the medical profession.

And then cholera struck once more.

The second great cholera epidemic to hit Britain began in Afghanistan. It swept through the Middle East, and then across Eastern and Western Europe, like a vengeful army, felling thousands. It arrived in Southwark, on the Thames, in September 1848, almost certainly brought by a sailor who had picked up the infection in Germany.

All across Europe people watched its approach with horror. Every city, town and village awaited its arrival with a potent mixture of rational fear and superstitious dread.

The sickness had many common names, but probably the one which best conveyed the general despairing belief in its all-conquering power was King Cholera.

King Cholera, a malevolent tyrant – invisible, and apparently totally indestructible.

King Cholera

T HE FEAR OF CHOLERA WAS far greater than simple fear of death. Death had always been a regular visitor – and many illnesses that are rarely fatal now were frequently fatal in nineteenth century Britain. So death, although not at all welcome, didn't carry the full aura of horror. It was the manner of death by cholera that was responsible for the dread and terror – that, and the sense of total helplessness.

When cholera struck, it struck suddenly – and often at night, so people were afraid of going to bed, as though staying up might somehow ward it off.

The principal characteristic of cholera is copious diarrhoea and vomiting. Almost at once, the diarrhoea becomes colourless and watery, and pours out in great quantity, shortly becoming the so-called 'rice water stools' that look like water with minute white filaments in it. (The filaments, it is now known, are part of the mucous membrane that lines the bowels.) There is extreme pain from terrible cramps in the stomach, and in other muscles too, as the body loses fluid and essential salts.

Temperature and blood pressure drop. The patient turns a bluish colour, the skin becomes cold and starts to shrivel, the eyes sink into the head and the whole body caves in.

The most dangerous aspect of cholera is the overwhelming fluid loss. The blood literally dries and thickens so that it can no longer circulate properly, and dehydration causes the kidneys to fail.

Killing the organism that causes cholera is only part of the answer. Modern treatment, which some nineteenth century doctors were already using, is the rapid replacement of fluids and essential salts, usually intravenously. Unless the fluids and salts can be replaced, the victim will die.

Even after death the muscles can continue to contract in severe spasms, so that the body writhes and thrashes after all life has gone. During the great cholera epidemics, this grisly fact gave rise to false hopes that the victim was not dead – and, even more, to a terror that people were being nailed into coffins while still alive. The terrible truth is that this may even have happened, so desperate were the survivors to get rid of the bodies, and the disease with them.

There was also an almost overpowering dread of hospitals, because so very few sufferers came out alive – and this dread extended to doctors. Not only did most doctors seem powerless to do much to help, there was also a widespread belief that some doctors were so keen to extend their knowledge of medicine that they might actually dissect people before they were dead.

In Britain, gruesome tales were still circulating about the ghastly activities of Burke and Hare in Edinburgh at the end of the 1820s. They had begun by robbing graves to supply dissecting theatres with corpses, and ended by murdering at least fifteen people in order to sell the bodies to the surgeons.

In some areas there were riots, with people storming hospitals in an attempt to liberate the inmates who they believed were being experimented upon.

During the first half of the nineteenth century there were three major cholera epidemics: the first originating in India, the second in Afghanistan, the third flaring out from the Baltic ports. As the disease stormed through Europe, desperate attempts were made to stop it spreading. The least drastic moves were to close all theatres, cancel public meetings and shorten church services. (No one wanted to cancel church services completely, in case that made the Almighty less likely to help.)

More dramatically, armies were often called in to try to control the spread of disease with guns. Throughout Europe, soldiers were stationed around infected villages, under orders to shoot anyone trying to leave. Troops lined frontiers to prevent anyone from crossing, whether infected or not – because who knew who might carry the infection? A person could be apparently totally healthy one moment, in a state of agonized collapse the next.

These may seem extreme reactions – but at that time no one knew how cholera spread. All anyone knew was that it followed human movement – along roads and highways and over the sea in ships. It seemed that the only way to contain it was to prevent all travel.

In the general atmosphere of panic and distress, irrational fears took hold. No one could deny that the disease struck the poor in vast numbers while the rich were noticeably less affected, and a rumour travelled rapidly across Europe. The ruling classes, it was said, were deliberately spreading the disease in order to reduce the population.

In his book *King Cholera*, Norman Longmate writes: "In Hungary the peasants captured the servants of some of the nobility who had shut themselves up in their castles and tortured them on the rack until they 'confessed' and swore oaths implicating their employers. A similar story arose in Berlin where it was rumoured that there was no such disease as cholera at all. It was instead an invention of the English who had used it to conceal their large scale poisoning of the population of India and were now being copied by the Governments of Europe."

Cholera cases were buried very deep, in a part of the churchyard away from other graves, for fear that healthy people visiting gravesides would be felled by emanations rising from the cholera-ridden corpses below.

As in most disasters, there were people who behaved with extreme brutality, and others who showed extraordinary kindness and heroism. At worst, fear brought about great cruelty. People were turned out of their lodgings if they showed signs of the illness. Sick travellers were thrown into the street to die without help. The seriously ill were beaten to death in an attempt to rid an area of the disease. Houses where there had been a cholera death were burnt to the ground.

At best, doctors, clergymen and ordinary families showed great dedication and heroism, working round the clock to care for the sick, often until they literally fell down with exhaustion, and sometimes until they caught the disease themselves and died of it. And, too, there was the kindness and generosity of families who already had many children, and were already living in extreme poverty, who would take in cholera orphans and bring them up as their own.

Although it was known that cholera followed human movement, it was not known how. Also no one could explain why it seemed to dance about so capriciously – striking a village but by-passing the next; singling out one house in a street, then leaping a block and attacking another dwelling a little distance away.

There were numerous theories – some building on others, some excluding others. The commonest of all the theories, and the one with most official support, was that cholera was carried in the air, as a miasma, as insubstantial and unstoppable as a ghost, but a thousand times more deadly.

On the other hand there were those who were convinced it took the form of a fungus. Others believed that the newly discovered electrical energy was at fault, and that either the electrical energy attracted the 'animacules' or organisms of cholera, or else that the electrical energy in some way actually created the cholera organism and then spread it.

The ozone theory was linked to the electrical theory. This suggested that ozone was a useful disinfectant, and that therefore lack of it allowed disease to flourish. Low levels of electrical activity in the atmosphere meant a low level of ozone – and, it was argued, greater risk of disease.

The connection between cholera and unhygienic living conditions had already been made. It was widely accepted that low-lying and poor areas were chiefly at risk, and most people believed that a cholera victim was as infectious dead as alive. But the actual method by which the disease was communicated from one person to another was unknown.

The beliefs of the miasmatists, although incorrect, were totally logical. It was all too obvious that once there was one case of cholera in an area, more always followed – so, clearly, cholera must be either infectious or contagious. It always seemed to flourish in low-lying, poorly drained areas where sanitation and hygiene of any sort were strangers. In these areas there was always the most appalling stench, often so powerful that those coming in from cleaner areas – doctors or clergymen for example – felt sick and faint as it hit them. So it was hard to avoid the conclusion that the disease was created in, and spread by, this airborne stench of putrefaction and decay.

The one thing that miasmatism didn't explain, though, was why some people in an area caught cholera and others didn't. To account for this, the miasmatists concluded that some people had a predisposition to catch the disease, while others had a natural immunity. It was suggested that this predisposition could be the result of bad or insufficient food, exhaustion from long hours in factories and sweatshops, squalid living conditions – and even, some suggested, from immoral living.

There was also an idea that the fear of catching cholera weakened people and put them at greater risk – a belief that seemed certain to add fear of fear to fear of cholera.

Because of the widespread belief in miasmatism, an overcast 'low' sky brought terror and foreboding since it seemed certain to trap the evil miasma close to the ground. Among desperate attempts at prevention, walls were painted with a mixture of whitewash and lime, streets were washed with lime, and tar barrels were burned to purify the air.

A hideous disease, then, frighteningly mysterious, and one which the medical profession was desperate to stamp out.

The first great epidemic had hit Britain when John Snow was still an apprentice, working for Dr Hardcastle in Newcastle upon Tyne. By the time the second epidemic hit, in 1848, he was a fully qualified doctor, and was already collecting data and developing his own theory about the disease. He was not at all convinced by the miasma theory, still less by the idea of predisposition.

He wrote: "For want of knowing any other cause, epidemics were attributed, by the ancients, to the atmosphere, without any evidence; just as political and social events were believed to be occasioned by the stars.

"Now, as people are not only exposed to the atmosphere, as soldiers in battle are to bullets, but are actually immersed in it, as fishes are in the sea, it became necessary to explain why certain persons were attacked and others not attacked, and the word predisposition was used as affording an explanation.

"The alleged predisposition, however, was nothing visible or evident: like the elephant that supports the world in Hindu mythology, it was merely invented to remove a difficulty."

The atmosphere – the air – obviously affects everyone, but there is another element that is just as vital, and just as likely to be polluted, as air. And it was this element that John Snow suspected.

Meanwhile, important though it was to understand how cholera spread, it was now urgently necessary to help those it had already attacked. The Blue Death – King Cholera – was stalking the country again, and the coffin-makers were busy.

Chapter 4

Chloroforming a Queen

BRITAIN WAS SLIGHTLY BETTER PREPARED for the second cholera epidemic than for the first – a Public Health Act had set up a General Board of Health. Still, the sickness was as savage as before, and its spread as unpredictable.

A London surgeon, Gideon Mantell, wrote in his journal, "All the shops are closed, and there are services in the churches to pray for protection from cholera, the sewers, ditches and other abominations."

The parish of St James, where John Snow lived and worked, was almost untouched by the pestilence, as it had been during the last epidemic, also. There was a reason for this, and William Farr, the Chief Statistician of the newly formed Office of the Registrar-General, worked out what it was.

The Registrar-General's office registered births, marriages and deaths, and Farr was able to produce detailed statistics of cholera deaths in London. These suggested that altitude was crucial. The higher above the Thames an area stood, the fewer deaths from cholera it would suffer. Later, he was able to show that this was true of the whole of England. The parish of St James was sixty feet above Thames high water, and the second cholera epidemic did only a little damage there, or in other high places.

Even though there was no cholera immediately around him, John Snow helped to care for the sick farther afield. He saw the disease at first hand yet again – and he found the Miasma Theory less and less convincing.

If the cholera poison was inhaled from the stinking miasma of some cesspool or open drain, he reasoned, then the first symptoms would surely be fever and headaches. But in cholera the first symptoms were always diarrhoea and vomiting. And all the other horrible effects of the disease – the blueness of the skin, the shrinking of the body, the agonizing cramps – were directly caused by this drastic loss of fluid. It seemed absolutely clear to him that the cholera poison must strike the alimentary canal first, not the lungs. Therefore, it must be taken in by mouth. And the most likely source was water – water tainted by the outpourings from people whose bodies were desperately trying to rid themselves of the cholera toxins.

The fact that disease could be carried by contaminated bedding and clothes was already well known. It was a grisly lesson that had been learned during the plague years. John Snow, obviously, knew this too, and he was also quite certain that people who cared for the sick and didn't wash before eating, passed the seeds of cholera into their mouths from their own hands. It wasn't that he thought infected drinking water was the only source, but that it was the principal and most important source.

He collected more data, and published *On the Mode of Communication of Cholera* in 1849. It didn't arouse much interest, and by the end of 1849 the cholera epidemic had burned itself out and gone, taking with it the lives of more than 14,000 Londoners.

***

John Snow had been working extraordinarily hard, even by his own standards, and he took a year off in 1851, the year of The Great Exhibition.

Its full title was 'The Great Exhibition of the Works of Industry of All Nations', displayed in Sir Joseph Paxton's vast and elegant glass and iron exhibition hall in Hyde Park, a construction so huge that it enclosed three of the Park's elm trees as well as more than 100,000 exhibits from all over the world.

Before it opened there were objections. It was said it would spoil Hyde Park; that it would attract 'rats, vagabonds and foreigners'; that high winds would shatter the glass and the sun shining through it would start fires.

But it was a huge success.

London was packed with tourists. The young Thomas Cook organised railway excursions from out of town. And between its opening on 1st May and its final day on 11th October, the glittering structure drew more than six million visitors – among them John Snow, who went several times with several friends. Chances are he also went with his much-loved uncle, Charles Empson, who certainly visited him in London quite often.

Benjamin Richardson wrote: "The year of the world's fair in London, 1851, may be considered a fortunate one for Dr Snow. His affairs had taken a new turn and the tide was fairly in his favour. He had a positive holiday, physical and mental ... old friends flocked around him, brought to the grand show in town, and all was well."

Outside this 'grand show in town' there were barrel organs, jugglers, Punch and Judy shows, and street traders selling oranges, ginger beer and souvenirs. Inside there were palatial halls filled with working machinery and steam engines, demonstrations of electricity and photography, a whole gallery of stained glass, and dazzling collections of precious stones, including the famous Koh-i-Noor diamond, lent by Queen Victoria.

There were elegant fountains; the central one made of nearly four tons of crystal. There were rifles, muskets and ceremonial sabres. In the North Gallery there was a large display of surgical instruments for the medically minded.

There was porcelain from France; Indian corn, pianos, cotton and furs from the United States; maple sugar and sleighs from Canada.

From the East Indies came leopard skins, sugars and spices, opium and tobacco; and from Russia, among the fine gold and silver ornaments, soap dishes made from rabbit's fur, lacquered to make them watertight.

And everywhere there were tropical plants, statues and carvings. Among the small statuettes were two inspired by Charles Dickens's books – figures of Oliver Twist, and of Little Nell and her grandfather.

Dickens himself found the whole experience exhausting and bewildering because the exhibition was so huge and so full of so many different things. He wrote to a friend, "...when anyone says 'Have you seen...?', I say 'Yes', because if I don't, I know he'll explain it, and I can't bear that!"

John Snow's several visits suggest he was delighted rather than bewildered, and wanted to enjoy everything the show had to offer. And then, after his year off, when he seems to have made up for all the holidays he'd missed during the years of studying and becoming established as a doctor, he returned to the work he loved.

By now, his reputation as an anaesthetist was so well known that he was called in to give anaesthetic to Queen Victoria to ease the birth of her eighth child, Prince Leopold.

A few years earlier, in 1847, he had published a book describing the uses of ether and the construction of his own ether inhaler. The book was well thought of, and sold rather nicely at first – but then James Young Simpson, the Professor of Obstetrics at Edinburgh University, pioneered the use of chloroform in Britain. Chloroform swiftly became more popular than ether, and the book sank into obscurity.

This doesn't seem to have slowed John Snow down. He was always interested in the new. He immediately ran tests on chloroform for himself – and, with his usual thoroughness, on himself. So by now he was using chloroform exclusively.

He had first been approached by the palace three years earlier, when the Queen was about to give birth to Prince Arthur, but nothing came of that. Anaesthesia was still a very new technique – and there was a tremendous swell of public opinion against anything that eased the pain of childbirth. After all, didn't the Bible say that, because of Eve's behaviour in the Garden of Eden, women should 'bring forth children in sorrow'?

This time, it happened. At her special request, and by permission of her doctor Sir James Clark,

John Snow administered chloroform to the Queen.

His notes at the time, though very discreet, record that "the Queen appeared very cheerful and well, expressing herself much gratified with the effect of the chloroform." In her own journal the Queen wrote that chloroform was "soothing, quieting and delightful beyond measure".

Later that same year, Dr Snow administered chloroform to the Archbishop of Canterbury's daughter when she had her baby.

Attitudes were already beginning to change, and the fact that chloroform seemed to have both the royal seal of approval and the blessing of the established church, had its effect. Before very long, pain relief came to be seen as a perfectly respectable, and even essential, part of medicine.

But something else happened in 1853, something altogether less pleasant. That summer, Asiatic cholera arrived in London for the third time. Shortly afterwards, it reached Newcastle. There it hit with great ferocity, and at least 1,500 people died. In London, though, there were only a few scattered cases during the second half of

1853, and the first half of 1854.

It wasn't until July of 1854 that the risk in London began to increase significantly, and 133 deaths were recorded. However, as before, the higher parts of London – the parish of St James among them – remained clear of the disease.

Then, on the 29th of August 1854, a baby girl living at No. 40 Broad Street, Soho, in the heart of St James's parish, became ill. Her parents thought she had summer diarrhoea. Sadly, her parents were wrong.

*Death in
the River*

BY THE TIME THE FULL EPIDEMIC struck in
Soho, on the last day of August 1854, it had
been flaring up in various parts of London for
several weeks and John Snow's attention was
already focused on it.

Later he wrote: "When the cholera returned to
London in July [1854] ... I resolved to spare no
exertion which might be necessary to ascertain
the exact effect of the water supply on the
progress of the epidemic ... I felt that the
circumstance of the cholera-poison passing down
the sewers into a great river, and being distributed
through miles of pipes ... was a fact of so startling

a nature, and of so vast importance to the community, that it could not be too rigidly examined ... "

He had never argued that cholera was solely carried in the water supply. He knew there was at least one other way in which the infection could get into the body. Quite simply, in the mid-nineteenth century people didn't wash much – and in the packed rookeries of the big cities some rarely washed at all, if ever. It was very many years before the basic practice of washing hands before meals caught on. Couple that with the quantity of outpourings from cholera patients and the fact that many of the sick were nursed at home, in one room with the rest of the family ...

The fluid carrying the infection got on to the hands of the carers as they tried to help the patient and deal with the sodden bedding. Because it was colourless, and didn't smell, no one was particularly aware of it. Hands passed it to food, and the food carried it into the mouth and straight down to the intestines ready to start a whole new cycle. (Doctors and clergy who worked during the epidemics were more fastidious, washed thoroughly and regularly, and rarely caught the disease.)

However, although he knew cholera was carried in other ways, John Snow remained convinced that it was chiefly water-borne. Trying to convince people of the importance of hygiene was crucial, but so was making sure that the water coming into every house, by whatever means, was free from infection.

He wasn't by any means the only person to think clean drinking water was important. Doctors, social reformers, bishops, members of the House of Commons and the House of Lords – most of them miasmatists – all agreed that filth, in water or elsewhere, was a serious problem and a cause of sickness. But they still believed the infection was bred in dirt and carried in airborne stench. The general view was that dirty drinking water could make people vulnerable to infection. Few were willing to consider that the water could actually carry the infection itself.

Proof was needed, and John Snow set himself

to investigate the effects of the different qualities of water supplied by different water companies.

Benjamin Richardson wrote, "No one but those who knew him intimately can conceive how he laboured, at what cost, and at what risk. Wherever cholera was visitant [in London] there was he in the midst."

Snow was particularly interested in two south London water companies: Lambeth, and Southwark-and-Vauxhall.

The Lambeth Water Company, which used to draw its water from the Thames in the heart of London, had obeyed the Metropolis Water Act of 1852, requiring water companies to shift their intakes upriver, above the tidal reach. This meant they would avoid the raw sewage (and other unknown and invisible horrors) which swilled up and down the lower part of the river. The Lambeth Company was now drawing clean water from a spot near Thames Ditton.

On the other hand, the Southwark-and-Vauxhall Water Company was still using the river at Battersea, near Vauxhall Bridge, a stretch which was as heavily polluted as any.

It was a huge investigation – a look at the map of the area, on which he noted every cholera death, shows just how huge – and it wasn't at all straightforward.

The two companies were serving the same part of south London, in direct competition with each other. There were some districts that were served exclusively by one or the other, but there were others that the two companies shared. In the shared areas, their pipes frequently ran side by side under the same streets, each supplying a proportion of the houses. There was no logic to the source of supply – of two houses on the same side of a street, joined in a terrace, one might be supplied by Lambeth, the other by Southwark-and-Vauxhall.

Instances of cholera from which the victim recovered were not always recorded, but deaths from cholera were. John Snow began by approaching the General Register Office, for the addresses of all who had died of cholera in the areas where the source of supply was easy to pinpoint. This showed that there were considerably more cholera deaths among people using Southwark-and-Vauxhall water.

He passed this information on to William Farr, the Chief Statistician for the Registrar General. Farr immediately approached the individual Registrars of the districts where it was so hard to disentangle the two suppliers. He asked to be informed which company supplied each house where a death from cholera had been recorded.

This was useful, but Snow didn't feel able to wait for the few weeks it would take for the details to come through. He continued his own researches, visiting houses and interviewing the occupants. Though he got up early, and worked until late in the evening, he couldn't do as much as he wanted and eventually he paid for professional help. He needed help not only because he'd taken all this upon himself, as well as caring for cholera victims and other patients, but also because of the high number of deaths he wanted to investigate, and the fact that interviews took time and patience. Even then it was often hard to get the information he needed.

The people he spoke to had, inevitably, just been bereaved, and were also coping with the fear that the disease would strike someone else in the house. And quite often they simply didn't know where their water came from – especially if they were renting rooms and an absentee landlord was paying the water bills.

Still, although people might not know who supplied their water, they often knew when it was available on tap. He checked at what times the "turncocks of both Companies visited any street", and sometimes got the answer he needed by that method.

His detective work didn't stop there. After experimenting with water known to come from one or other of the companies, he developed a chemical test that meant he could "distinguish the water of the two companies with perfect certainty". He added solution of nitrate of silver to the water. Nitrate of silver changes into chloride of silver in the presence of chloride of sodium. So by measuring the quantity of chloride of silver, he could discover the quantity of sodium chloride present – and sodium chloride, common salt, is a by-product of human waste.

The net result of Dr Snow's researches was this. "Whilst only 563 deaths occurred from cholera in the whole Metropolis in the four weeks ending 5th August, more than half of them took place amongst the customers of the Southwark-and-Vauxhall Water Company, and a great proportion of the remaining deaths were those of mariners and persons employed among the shipping in the Thames, who almost invariably drew their drinking water from the river."

John Snow was already preparing a new and fuller edition of *On the Mode of Communication of Cholera* for publication at the end of the year. In it he wrote: "No fewer than three hundred thousand people of both sexes, of every age and occupation, and of every rank and station, from gentle folks down to the very poor, were divided into two groups without their choice, and, in most cases, without their knowledge; one group being supplied with water containing the sewage of London, and, amongst it, whatever might have come from the cholera patients, the other group having water quite free from such impurity."

And then, on 31st August 1854, a violent storm of cholera broke in the previously cholera-free area of Soho. In Broad Street alone, 56 people died of it.

"The most terrible outbreak of cholera which ever occurred in this kingdom," John Snow wrote, "is probably that which took place in Broad Street, Golden Square, and the adjoining streets, a few weeks ago.

"Within two hundred and fifty yards of the spot where Cambridge Street joins Broad Street, there were upwards of five hundred fatal attacks of cholera in ten days. The mortality in this limited area probably equals any that was ever caused in this country, even by the plague; and it was much more sudden, as the greater number of cases terminated in a few hours.

"The mortality would undoubtedly have been much greater had it not been for the flight of the population. Persons in furnished lodgings left first, then other lodgers went away, leaving their furniture to be sent for when they could meet with a place to put it in. Many houses were closed altogether, owing to the death of the proprietors; and, in a great number of instances, the tradesmen who remained had sent away their families: so that in less than six days from the commencement of the outbreak, the most afflicted streets were deserted by more than three-quarters of their inhabitants."

At first the streets must have been full of agitation and activity as those who were still healthy left, some carrying their belongings, some using carts or maybe carriages.

Others, less fortunate, would have been on the move too, in rather different ways. A few who had faith in the medical profession – or perhaps were just too weak to resist – would have been carried or carted to one of the central London hospitals. Rather more would have been on the final journey to the grave.

Later, the streets would have been oddly quiet and empty.

For a concerned doctor, which Snow certainly was, the Soho outbreak was more intense and shocking than anything that had happened in any other part of the country. But from a scientific point of view it offered an excellent opportunity for research because the affected area was so small.

Snow set himself the task of tracking down something that had eluded doctors for centuries. Something he knew could travel across countries and oceans and could strike suddenly and extraordinarily violently. Something he knew was all around him, unknown, invisible – deadly.

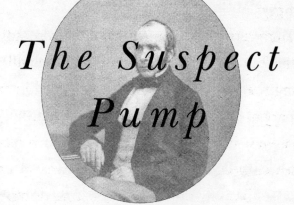

Chapter 6

The Suspect Pump

D R SNOW NO LONGER LIVED in Soho itself. He'd moved in 1853 to a house at No. 18 Sackville Street. Sackville Street, just off Piccadilly, was smarter than Frith Street. Here we know he employed a housekeeper, who stayed with him for the rest of his life, and it is highly likely that there was some other domestic help as well.

From Sackville Street it was not far to the heart of Soho, especially to someone so accustomed to walking as he was. He would only have had to cross Regent Street, possibly walk through the pleasant green area in the centre of Golden Square, and turn a couple of corners to reach

Broad Street itself.

Helping the sick was the priority.

Because antibiotics were not yet available it was impossible to attack the disease itself – patients only survived if their bodies were strong enough to throw off the infection themselves.

Over the years many treatments had been tried. Some doctors prescribed a purgative called calomel. It may seem odd that they gave a purgative to someone who already had violent diarrhoea, but the idea was to rid the body of whatever was poisoning it as soon as possible. Some gave opium for the pain of the terrible cramps, though others thought this a bad idea because opium makes the blood flow more slowly, and the blood was already sluggish because it was drying up.

Other, less conventional, treatments included a wide strip of flannel wrapped around the waist 'to draw out the poison through the skin', and ice packs on the spine.

But the more enlightened doctors of Snow's time knew the most important thing was to get as much fluid as possible into the sufferer – because the dehydration was quite as dangerous as the infection. Snow would also have tried, in his quiet way, to persuade whoever was caring for the victim that hygiene was vital – and he would have washed his hands at the end of every visit. He understood very well that people living in such cramped and filthy conditions didn't find it easy to follow his advice about cleanliness – but he could hardly fail to tell them something so important.

But as well as all his other work, he began to examine the water supply with his usual thoroughness.

Every house in Soho was already on the mains. Some got water from the New River Company whose source was in Hertfordshire, and some from the Grand Junction Water Company which took water from the Thames at Kew. Both of these sources were regarded as clean. However – as was usual at that time – the companies only supplied water for a couple of hours each day and none on Sunday. Some of the residents stored water, but most relied on public supplies. There were numerous shallow wells under the streets of Soho, each fitted with a cast-iron pump. Most of the pumps were used regularly and some, those that seemed to give sweeter water, were used more frequently than others.

John Snow noted that: "There were a few cases of cholera in the neighbourhood of Broad Street, Golden Square, in the latter part of August, and the so-called outbreak, which commenced in the night between the 31st August and the 1st September, was, as in all similar instances, only a violent increase of the malady.

"As soon as I became acquainted with the situation and extent of this irruption of cholera, I suspected some contamination of the water of the much-frequented street-pump in Broad Street, near the end of Cambridge Street."

Suspicion of contamination was not enough, though. If official action was to be taken about the pump there would have to be proof – doctor would have to continue to act as detective.

Dr Snow began to take samples from the pump at Broad Street at various times of day, and carry

Picture 1: A photograph of John Snow.

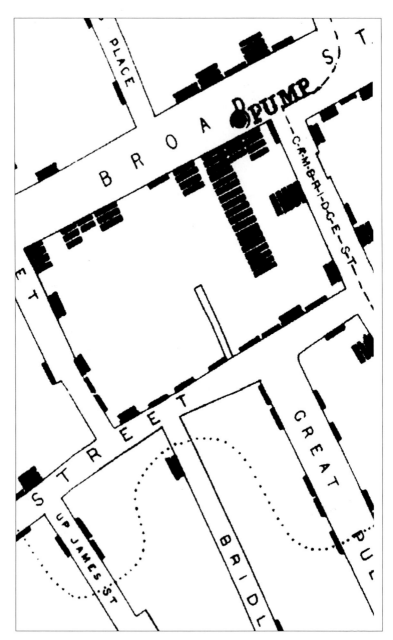

Picture 2: A map of Soho drawn by John Snow. The black oblongs show cholera deaths around the Broad Street pump.

Picture 3: A section of a London map published in 1851. It looks
south (instead of north) across Soho, from Oxford Street down to
Trafalgar Square. (Regent Circus is now called Piccadilly Circus.)
You can see many of the streets mentioned in this book – Soho
Square, Broad Street (and the brewery building), Golden Square,
Berwick Street, Carnaby Street and Frith Street – but you may
need a magnifying glass to help you pick them out!

Picture 4. The pump with r
handle is a replica of the
original Broad Street pump
stands in Broadwick Street
Soho, London – 'wick' was
added to 'Broad' in 1936,
because there were several
other Broad Streets in Lon

The Red Granite kerbstone
marks the site of the historic
BROAD STREET PUI
associated with Dr John Snow
discovery in 1854
that Cholera is conveyed by wa

Picture 5. The plaque commemorates
John Snow's work, and says exactly
where the original pump stood.

them back to his study in his Sackville Street house to examine them carefully. At first he couldn't see anything to confirm his suspicions, but on the other hand he couldn't think of any other possible source of the poison.

By 3rd September, the fourth day of the outbreak, the pump water seemed clear and he began to have doubts. Still, he continued to check it, and during the next two days, (4th and 5th September) he noticed a number of tiny white floating particles.

He asked a colleague, Dr Hassall, to examine a sample of the water through a microscope, and Dr Hassall saw minute scraps of 'organic matter'. At that time the existence of bacteria was suspected, though not called by that name and not yet identified or recognisable. (The cholera bacterium was isolated in 1883 by a German doctor and bacteriologist, Robert Koch.)

Still, there was definitely something in the water, even if it wasn't possible at that time to say what it was.

In the past, when it had been argued that cholera couldn't be carried in water because not everyone drinking the same water became ill, Snow had pointed out that the cholera poison was unlikely to be so thoroughly mixed with the water that every drop would hold the same amount. He also thought it likely (and later research proved him right) that if water was left to stand for any length of time the poison would sink to the bottom, and that water taken from near the top of the container would be safe.

So now he decided that though the water had seemed clear when he first examined it, it might have looked very different just before the outbreak.

"I requested permission, therefore, to take a list, at the General Register Office, of the deaths from cholera, registered during the week ending 2nd September, in the subdistricts of Golden Square, Berwick Street and St Ann's, Soho, which was kindly granted." The death of the baby girl at No. 40 Broad Street was listed with the rest, but not until months later did it take on any special significance.

By this time, Tuesday 5th September, the rate of infection (and with it the death rate) though still terrifyingly high, was beginning to drop. Even so, the three hospitals nearest to Soho – the Middlesex, Charing Cross and University College Hospitals – were almost overwhelmed by the number of patients. And this despite the fact that most sufferers struggled with the disease in their own homes, and survived or died there.

Over that first terrible weekend alone, the Middlesex took in 120 cholera victims, the vast majority from the Soho area. Extra nurses were called in from wherever they could be spared – among them Florence Nightingale, who was then in charge of the Institute for Sick Gentlewomen in Harley Street.

(This was the month, September 1854, which saw the beginning of the Crimean War, and in two months' time Florence Nightingale would be on her way to the Crimea, to the hospital at Scutari near Constantinople. She was, and remained to the end of her life, a believer in the miasma theory of disease – but like so many of the miasmatists, she also believed in the crucial importance of hygiene.)

Once Dr Snow had a list of the addresses of all the fatal cases in the Soho area, he could see a clear pattern. "Eighty-nine deaths from cholera were registered, during the week, in the three subdistricts. Of these, only six occurred in the four first days of the week; four occurred on Thursday 31st August; and the remaining seventy-nine on Friday and Saturday. I considered, therefore, that the outbreak commenced on the Thursday; and I made inquiry, in detail, respecting the eighty-three deaths registered as having taken place during the last three days of the week."

Although the area in question was so very much smaller than the South London districts he was also studying, the house to house enquiries still presented difficulties, simply because not everyone was available to ask. Some had fled the area, some were too sick to speak, some had died. Nevertheless he collected enough information to confirm his suspicions of the Broad Street pump.

"On proceeding to the spot, I found that nearly all the deaths had taken place within a short distance of the pump. There were only ten deaths in houses situated decidedly nearer to another street pump. In five of these cases the families of the deceased persons informed me that they always sent to the pump in Broad Street, as they preferred the water to that of the pump which was nearer. In three other cases, the deceased were children who went to school near the pump in Broad Street. Two of them were known to drink the water; and the parents of the third think it probable that it did so. The other two deaths, beyond the district which this pump supplies, represent only the amount of mortality from cholera that was occurring before the irruption took place."

On the evening of Thursday 7th September, the Board of Guardians of St James's parish held a meeting to discuss the outbreak. (The Boards of Guardians of the various parishes managed local public affairs – much as local councils do today – often working with a local trust that might be responsible, for example, for street lighting, paving or water supplies, and they were also responsible for handing out Poor Relief.)

Dr Snow asked to be admitted to this meeting, and he presented his findings to the Board. The Board was thoroughly sceptical, but nevertheless agreed to have the handle of the pump removed on the following day.

Popular myth – which is often more fun than the truth – says that, once John Snow was certain the pump was contaminated, he broke its handle off himself. He didn't. However well justified, that would have been an act of vandalism, and completely out of character. He went through the proper channels, as always.

Popular myth also says that from the moment the handle of the pump was removed, the cholera epidemic in Soho began to fade. That's a nice story, too, and it would have been useful to Snow if it had happened that way because it would have helped to confirm that he was right. But it isn't true – and certainly Snow himself never claimed that it was.

The handle was removed on 8th September, a day on which 'only' thirty people died. Thirty-two had died on 7th, thirty-seven on 6th, forty-five on the 5th, seventy-one on the 4th, seventy-six on 3rd and, on 2nd September, the worst day, one hundred and twenty-seven had died.

Dr Snow already knew the epidemic was burning itself out when he applied to have the pump immobilised – but he was still certain the pump had been the source of it all, and was determined that it shouldn't have the chance to rekindle the horror.

He was perfectly well aware that the Board of Guardians had only agreed to take the pump out of service to be on the safe side, not because they truly believed there was a problem with it. What was more, he was well aware that they didn't even accept the idea of cholera being carried in contaminated water. In common with the majority of people, they were still convinced by the miasma theory – and the stench in Soho, with its leaking cesspools, often cramped living conditions, piles of rotting rubbish, and cattle –

alive or recently slaughtered – seemed strong enough to carry any amount of disease through the foetid air.

In spite of all he had done, in spite of all his researches, he had not been able to prove that cholera was water-borne. It's easy to imagine someone giving up at that point – but Snow was patient, determined and convinced he was right. He understood that more proof was needed, and he set out to find it.

Chapter 7

The Map of Death

WHEN JOHN SNOW TOOK UP the Broad Street pump enquiry again, the Soho episode was fading. Although deaths continued until September 29th, they were the deaths of people who had contracted the disease much earlier.

By 15th September the worst was over according to *The Times* of that date, which reported: "The outbreak of cholera in the vicinity of Golden Square is now subsiding but the passenger through the streets which compass that district will see many evidences of the alarming severity of the attack. Men and women in mourning are to be found in great numbers, and the chief topic of conversation is the recent epidemic..."

The newspaper article added that quantities of lime were still very evident, "... and the air is redolent with its strong and not very agreeable odour. The parish authorities have very wisely determined to wash all the streets of the tainted district with this powerful disinfectant; accordingly the purification takes place regularly each evening. The shop keepers have dismal stories to tell – how they would hear in the evening that one of their neighbours whom they had been talking with in the morning had expired after a few hours of agony and torture. It has even been asserted that the number of corpses was so great that they were removed wholesale in dead-carts for want of sufficient hearses to convey them; but let us hope this is incorrect."

Unfortunately, it wasn't incorrect. The huge death toll, in a small area, in the short space of two weeks, produced too many bodies to be coped with in the more usual, and more dignified, way.

Dr Snow got back to his investigations with a certain amount of anxiety that the trail might have gone cold. So many people had died, or moved away permanently, that he was afraid he wasn't going to be able to get a full enough picture.

"I found that there had been such a distribution of the remaining population that it would be impossible to arrive at a complete account of the circumstances. There is no reason to suppose, however, that a more extended inquiry would have yielded a different result..."

And so he got on with it.

(Joshua Parsons had been right about his "indomitable perseverance and determination in following up whatever line of investigation was open to him", though he seems to have missed the mark when he wrote that Snow was "not particularly quick of apprehension or ready in invention". Even though his conviction that cholera was water-borne was only accepted by a limited number of medical men and others during his life-time, still he was well respected for the papers and articles he published, for his work as an anaesthetist, and for his inventions of medical apparatus for helping new born babies with breathing problems and for administering anaesthetics.)

To support his theory, John Snow settled down in his upstairs study with a street map of the area and painstakingly marked every house where someone had died of cholera. He also marked the position of the Broad Street pump. The death-marks clustered tellingly around the pump and then radiated out from it, becoming less dense and more scattered as the distance from the pump increased.

Ironically, the pump in Broad Street was very popular. The water was reported to taste better than the water from other local pumps. In particular, the one at the end of Carnaby Street produced such unpleasant water that almost everyone avoided it (and it turned out that the people who died of cholera in the houses closest to the Carnaby Street pump had always chosen to fetch water from Broad Street).

Studying the map and the addresses of victims, Dr Snow noticed some oddities that seemed at first to throw his theory into doubt.

For one thing, the Workhouse in Poland Street, just round the corner from Broad Street, was surrounded by cholera-deaths – but out of five hundred and thirty-five inmates, only five had died of it. He calculated that if the cholera-deaths in the Workhouse had followed the pattern of those outside, then more than a hundred should have died.

Only so much could be discovered, sitting at his study table late into the evening, examining his notes and his map by the light of an oil lamp. To disentangle the oddities, he had to go back to the streets of Soho, knock on more doors and ask more questions. In this way, he discovered that the workhouse had its own well on the premises, to supplement the usual intermittent mains supply, and never collected water from Broad Street.

He had also noticed that although the Red Lion Brewery in Broad Street was quite near the pump, no brewer's men had died of cholera. However, he only had a list of deaths, not a list of those who had suffered and recovered, so next he called on the proprietor, Mr Huggins, to enquire. Mr Huggins told him that of the seventy brewery workers only two had caught cholera; neither had been severely ill and both had recovered. However, the brewery, like the Workhouse had its own deep well, so there was never any call to use the outside pump. John Snow's notes state: "The men are allowed a certain quantity of malt liquor, and Mr Huggins believes they do not drink water at all..."

Then Dr Snow approached John Marshall, the surgeon, who lived in Greek Street, and asked him to follow up on seven men who had worked at a Dentists' Materials Manufactory at 8 and 9 Broad Street, and who had all died of cholera in their own homes elsewhere. Mr Marshall was able to confirm that all seven definitely drank from the pump every day.

At the Percussion Cap Manufactory, 37 Broad Street, though, not all the two hundred or so workers were so lucky. Mr Eley, the proprietor, confirmed that "two tubs were kept on the premises always supplied with water from the pump in the street, for those to drink who wished; and eighteen of these workpeople died of cholera at their own homes, sixteen men and two women."

Mr Eley offered an extra piece of useful information. He told Dr Snow "he had long noticed that the water became offensive, both to the smell and taste, after it had been kept about two days." Dr Snow added the comment, "This, as I noticed before, is a character of water contaminated with sewage."

Evidence was building, his notebook was filling.

Someone else who had noticed the offensive smell of the pump water just before Dr Snow began to examine it was John Gould, the ornithologist, who produced large and beautifully illustrated books on birds, including seven volumes of *The Birds of Australia* (and was, as it happens, the first person to bring live budgerigars back to England.) John Gould lived near the Broad Street pump and regularly used the water. Fortunately, he was away at the start of the outbreak, but he got home on the morning of 2nd September and at once sent for some of the water. "He was much surprised to find that it had an offensive smell, although perfectly transparent and fresh from the pump. He did not drink any of it. Mr Gould's assistant, Mr Prince, had his attention drawn to the water, and perceived its offensive smell. A servant of Mr Gould, who drank the pump water daily, and drank a good deal of it on August 31st, was seized with cholera at an early hour on September 1st. She ultimately recovered."

After exhaustive enquiries, John Snow was left with a very short list of names of people working or living locally who had died of cholera, but who had apparently not drunk from the dubious pump. He felt he could account for these to his own satisfaction – although he would have preferred proof.

"There are various ways," he wrote, "in which the deceased persons may have taken it without the knowledge of their friends. The water was used for mixing with spirits in all the public houses around. It was used likewise at dining-rooms and coffee-shops. The keeper of a coffee-shop in the neighbourhood, which was frequented by mechanics, and where the pump-water was supplied at dinnertime, informed me (on 6th September) that she was already aware of nine of her customers who were dead. The pump-water was also sold in various little shops, with a teaspoonful of effervescing powder in it, under the name of sherbet: and it may have been distributed in various other ways with which I am unacquainted."

Yet despite all this evidence, and despite the fact that by now he had other medical men on his side, his views were still not generally accepted.

The miasmatists continued to believe cholera was born and bred in the filth of the area, carried on the air, and breathed in by its victims.

Some even accused him of encouraging, or at least not condemning, 'nuisances' – a discreet term for filth and stench. This was particularly unfair because he always made it clear that hygiene was, literally, vital, and that he was well aware that it was bad for people to live in squalor and breathe in foul smells day and night. His argument was simply that this disease was carried in contaminated water, not in contaminated air.

And, perhaps inevitably, some of the local people were convinced the pestilence had crept out of a nearby plague pit – even though John Snow pointed out that the supposed pit was said to be in Little Marlborough Street, beyond the cholera area.

So much data, all of it dismissed. But then he came upon something that seemed to offer the strongest confirmation yet.

It was the curious case of the Hampstead Widow.

Chapter 8

The Case of the Hampstead Widow

REALLY STRONG PROOF WAS NEEDED that the Broad Street pump-well was contaminated with cholera – strong proof, firm proof, irrefutable proof. And the unfortunate Hampstead widow unwittingly provided it.

A medical friend of Dr Snow's, Dr Fraser, who lived in Oakley Square in North London, tipped him off about an entry in the *Weekly Return of Births and Deaths* for that area, published on 9th September. It recorded a death in Hampstead "At West End, on 2nd September, the widow of a percussion-cap maker, aged 59 years, diarrhoea two hours, cholera epidemica sixteen hours."

What was interesting about this was that Hampstead is on a hill. The whole area, north, south, east and west is on high ground. In common with other places which stood high above sea level, and high above the Thames valley, Hampstead was healthy, untouched by cholera. So this singular case was very surprising.

The woman who died was Mrs Susannah Eley, the widow of the original proprietor of the Percussion Cap Manufactory in Broad Street, which was now run by their son. It seemed perfectly possible that she had made the journey to Broad Street to visit her son and the factory – and equally possible that she'd had a drink of water while she was there.

However, when Dr Snow interviewed Mr Eley again, this time on the subject of his mother, he was told that she hadn't been to Broad Street for many months. But, as it turned out, Broad Street had gone to her.

"A cart went from Broad Street to West End every day, and it was the custom to take out a large bottle of the water from the pump in Broad

Street, as she preferred it. The water was taken on Thursday 31st August, and she drank of it in the evening, and also on Friday. She was seized with cholera on the evening of the latter day, and died on Saturday, as the above quotation from the register shows. A niece, who was on a visit to this lady, also drank of the water; she returned to her residence, in a high and healthy part of Islington, was attacked with cholera, and died also. There was no cholera at the time, either at West End or in the neighbourhood where the niece died."

Dr Snow felt this story was "perhaps the most conclusive of all in proving the connexion between the Broad Street pump and the outbreak of cholera".

The authorities didn't share his opinion, but even so the body of evidence was now strong enough to persuade them that someone should take a close look at the well served by the Broad Street pump. Eventually, the Parish Paving Committee authorised this – and on 27th November reported that they had found nothing wrong with it.

Dr Snow had a conversation with Mr Farrell, who was in charge of the opening up of the well. Mr Farrell told him it was about twenty-eight or thirty feet deep, and had been dug through gravel to the strata of London clay below, where water collected and was then pumped to the surface as needed. The nearby sewer was twenty-two feet below ground – so above the level of the well-water, and also several yards to one side of it. He confirmed that the brick walls of the well had been carefully examined, but that no hole or crack had been found which could let in any contamination.

When Dr Snow had examined the well water at the time of the cholera he had found that it "contained impurities of an organic nature, in the form of minute whiteish flocculi visible on close inspection to the naked eye, as I before stated. Dr Hassall, who was good enough to examine some of this water with the microscope, informed me that these particles had no organised structure, and that he thought they probably resulted from decomposition of other matter. He found a great number of very minute oval animalcules in the water, which are of no importance, except as an additional proof that the water contained organic matter on which they lived. The water also contained a large quantity of chlorides, indicating, no doubt, the impure sources from which the spring is supplied."

But it seemed that now, a couple of months later, there was no evidence of anything untoward. The pump was flushed out and the handle replaced.

The General Board of Health sent three inspectors to check the area. But it dismissed Dr Snow's hypothesis in its *Report on Scientific Enquiries*, part of which read: "The suddenness of the outbreak, the immediate climax and short duration, all point to some atmospheric or other widely diffused agent still to be discovered, and forbid the assumption in this instance, of any communication of the disease from person to person either by infection or contamination of water with the excretions of the sick...

"... In explanation of the remarkable intensity of this outbreak within very definite limits, it has been suggested by Dr Snow that the real cause of whatever was peculiar in the case lay in the general use of one particular well, situate at Broad Street in the middle of the district, and having (it was imagined) its waters contaminated by the rice-water evacuations of cholera patients. After careful inquiry we see no reason to adopt this belief. We do not find it established that the water was contaminated in the manner alleged..."

John Snow completed a second and far more detailed edition of *On the Mode of Communication of Cholera*, which included all his findings about the South London water companies and about the Soho outbreak. (The book came out the following year, and Benjamin Richardson says it was "...a work in the preparation and publication of which he spent more than £200 in hard cash, and realised in return scarcely so many shillings.")

John Snow may not have made a profit from the book, but that wasn't his purpose in writing it, and at least his life was somewhat easier now. He was earning a reasonable living, and perhaps his year off in 1851 had given him a taste for relaxation, because now he occasionally took an evening off to go to the opera. He didn't read novels – he preferred to spend reading time on scientific works – but he enjoyed listening when Benjamin Richardson read out funny passages from Dickens. He also found time to visit friends, and loved the company of their children. He admitted he regretted not marrying and having children of his own – but in the early years, when his friends were pairing off, he was too busy studying and establishing his practice to notice he was missing out.

And then, unexpectedly, the Vestry of St James appointed a committee to make a thorough enquiry, mainly into the Soho outbreak but also into the general sanitary conditions in the area for which they were responsible.

There was some opposition to this at first. The Board of Guardians, for example, tried to block it on the grounds that it would be an unnecessary expense and also might create distress and alarm among the local people who were only just beginning to recover, physically and emotionally. Despite this, though, the Cholera Inquiry Committee was formed, made up of eight vestrymen, six medical men, and two clergymen.

One of the medical men was Dr Edwin Lankester, who later became Medical Officer for Health for the parish of St James, another was Dr John Snow, and one of the clergymen was the man who, in the end, made the most important contribution of all to the inquiry – the 29-year old Curate of St Luke's in Berwick Street, the Reverend Henry Whitehead.

Naturally, Dr Snow made his book available to the committee, handing it first to the Reverend Whitehead who accepted it with thanks, was impressed by the body of evidence it contained – but was not convinced that cholera was spread in contaminated water. Whitehead later published his own account of the epidemic, and wrote that at the time of the formation of the Cholera Inquiry Committee "scarcely anyone seriously believed in [Snow's] theory. For my own part, when I first heard of it, I stated to a medical friend my belief that a careful investigation would refute it..."

A major new enquiry was all set to go. The long saga of the Broad Street pump was not over yet.

The Final Piece of the Puzzle

T HE MEMBERS OF THE CHOLERA Committee, Dr Snow and the Reverend Whitehead amongst them, carried out one of the most extensive enquiries ever undertaken. After a couple of setbacks they began work in January 1855, and their final report was ready by August of that year.

John Snow had focused his own investigation on the question: "Was the Broad Street pump the source of the cholera outbreak in Soho?"

The Committee worked with a more general and wider question: "What caused the cholera outbreak in Soho?" This meant checking everything. Henry

Whitehead wrote, "every local condition, therefore, of the infected district, such as elevation of site, nature of soil and subsoil, surface and ground plan, streets and courts, density and character of population, internal economy of houses, cesspools, house-drains, and sewerage, was minutely investigated."

The General Board of Health refused to supply a copy of its own report to the Committee, claiming it thought an independent inquiry was preferable.

However, John Snow submitted a brief report of his own, clarifying his position: "I wish it to be understood that I do not attribute every case of Cholera to the use of polluted water. It is my opinion that every case is caused by swallowing the peculiar poison or morbid matter of Cholera, which has proceeded from a previous patient sick of the malady; but this morbid matter need not be in water, and there are facilities for its being accidentally swallowed, and propagating the disease, without the aid of water. This is more especially the case in the crowded dwellings of the poor, where a number of persons live, sleep, cook and eat in one room. I do not, therefore, attribute every case of Cholera in the parish to the water of the pump well in Broad Street, but certainly those which constitute the great outbreak which took place at the end of August, and which suddenly raised the mortality of this disease from about five in a week to nearly 500."

The Cholera Committee was not convinced.

The Committee members divided the work amongst themselves. Henry Whitehead began to make house-to-house calls throughout the district, sometimes travelling miles to track down families who had left the area – often having to return to a house many times to catch up with residents who had been out when he called before – always trying to speak to each witness more than once, to check and double check all information.

He was as determined as any of them to uncover the true cause of the problem. During the heat of the outbreak he had spent his days visiting the afflicted and the bereaved, often encountering the "medical men of the neighbourhood – whose labours day and night in behalf of the sufferers were beyond all praise", and he was desperate for the mystery to be solved so that such a thing should never happen again.

Also, he was probably more determined than most to disprove John Snow's theory, simply because he was convinced it was wrong, and therefore misleading.

From the start, the facts of the case challenged the long-held views about cholera. Although the Reverend Whitehead didn't accept John Snow's new judgement, the shock of the outbreak made him begin to doubt some of the old judgements.

He especially came to dislike the suggestion that fear made people more likely to catch cholera. It was said that "pestilence slays its thousands but fear slays its tens of thousands." In fact, he didn't only dislike that saying, he found it positively offensive: "...having seen the brave and the timid indiscriminately dying and indiscriminately surviving, I had come to regard it as an insult to the memory of the dead, many of whom had behaved most heroically..."

Also, to his surprise, he found that it wasn't true that cholera only attacks people who are steeped in filth. "Three houses which had been singled out by the parochial authorities, during an inspection of the parish, for special commendation in the matter of cleanliness, were almost the only houses in one particular street which were visited by the disease, – one of them losing 12 of its inmates. On the other hand, the very filthiest house in the district...escaped without death...whilst, within a few yards of this house, a model lodging-house lost two of its inmates."

He and the rest of the Committee met regularly to share their findings.

They couldn't ignore the pattern of deaths – the way the greatest numbers were in those houses closest to the Broad Street pump.

They discovered all over again that people who had died a few streets away had always walked the extra distance to Broad Street, because they thought its well-water was the best in the area.

They were, of course, aware that the worst days had been between 31st August and 3rd September, by which time the epidemic, though still claiming many lives, was slowly beginning to fade.

At last they began to discuss the possibility of some kind of problem with the pump... IF the cholera contamination had come from the Broad Street pump well, they reasoned, then why did the epidemic die down after a few days? Could it be because the pump was so heavily used? IF pollution had somehow got into the water, then perhaps it had been pumped out over those few terrible days by residents made extra thirsty by the hot summer weather and drinking more than usual.

IF the Broad Street pump well had been contaminated, and the contamination had caused the outbreak, the poison must have polluted it around the 29th or 30th of August...

IF ... if...

To the surprise of all of them – apart from Dr Snow himself – the Committee members found that evidence against the suspect pump well was steadily accumulating.

And then, on 3rd April 1855, Henry Whitehead chanced to read a piece of information that struck him as extremely significant.

The extraordinary thing was that it was something he had read before – and something John Snow had almost certainly read before that.

But only now did its importance seem clear...

Whitehead was glancing through the lists of deaths for the area, in the Registrar's Returns, and found himself reading the words: "At 40 Broad Street, 2nd September, a daughter, aged five months, exhaustion after an attack of diarrhoea four days previous to death."

Four days previous to death – so the child must have been struck with cholera around 29th August. And No. 40 Broad Street was the house facing the pump-well.

Henry Whitehead went straight to 40 Broad Street and talked to the child's mother, who lived with the rest of her family in the back parlour. She told him "that the child was attacked on August 28th, and that the dejections at first were abundant, but ceased on the 30th. In answer to further questions, she told me that the dejections were collected in napkins, which, on being removed, were immediately steeped in pails, the water from which was poured partly into a sink in the back yard and partly into a cesspool in the front area."

All too aware of how close the cesspool was to

the pump well, the Reverend Whitehead went straight to the Committee with his findings. They ordered an immediate investigation.

This time, though, they didn't just open up the pump well itself – they actually dug up the earth pavement between the house and the well to check the drain, the sewer, the cesspool, everything.

What they found was horrific.

The main drain from the house was rotting. Its joints were crumbling; its brickwork was decaying. It was leaking like a sieve.

The cesspool attached to it had been built badly in the first place, and the passage of time had not improved it. Its brick walls leaked as heavily as the drain and its wooden lid was rotten and saturated.

And right beside both the drain and the cesspool, its water level a few feet below the level of the cesspool, was the well. Furrows of "saturated swampy soil" could clearly be seen leading directly into it.

The well itself had become a cesspool.

Would the authorities finally agree that the pump well was not only disgusting but also positively dangerous?

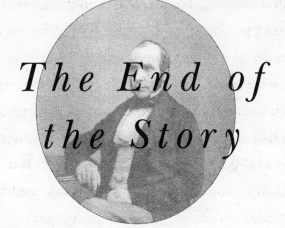

Chapter 10

The End of
the Story

Having gazed into the murky depths of
the Broad Street well, the shocked and
revolted committee took the necessary action, and
it was closed for good. The cholera epidemic was
over, but it was unthinkable that people should
continue to drink water from such a foul and
stinking source.

Henry Whitehead, who had set out to disprove
John Snow's theory, actually succeeded in
confirming it. He apologised at once and the two
became good friends.

John Snow had been proved right – but it's
worth remembering that he never claimed to have

stopped the Soho outbreak by having the pump-handle removed. He knew the epidemic was already burning itself out and would have come to a natural end anyway.

Or would it...?

It was now clear that the cholera outbreak in Soho had begun at No. 40 Broad Street, with the illness and death of the baby girl there. But when Henry Whitehead talked to her family and made the crucial breakthrough, he discovered something else, too.

The baby's father had collapsed with a bad case of cholera, from which he eventually died, on 8th September. The cholera-ridden discharges that poured out of him would inevitably have found their way into the cesspool and from there into the well, to be pumped up and drunk down by the unsuspecting. But the 8th September was the day on which the Vestry Committee, responding reluctantly to Dr Snow's warning, removed the handle and put the pump out of action.

There is no proof – and Dr Snow never accepted a theory without reasonable proof – but it seems highly likely that if the pump had still been in use, a whole new epidemic would have flared up in the rubbish-strewn streets of Soho in that long, hot summer.

Either way, the important thing is that John Snow never gave up. Even when the General Board of Health refused to accept his theory, he continued his steady efforts to persuade everyone who had the power to act that he was right.

The importance of his discovery is immeasurable. It has benefited the whole world. But it wasn't acknowledged at once. It was taken seriously only gradually, and although he was by now greatly respected for his work, especially his work with anaesthetics, John Snow wasn't widely acclaimed for his work on cholera during his lifetime.

It seems unlikely that this would have bothered him. He knew that belief in his theory was spreading, however slowly, and he knew that soon it would be possible to save thousands and thousands of people from the agony of the blue death. And that was what mattered to him.

In 1858, John Snow died. He was only forty-five years old.

His early death was blamed on various things, including his vegetarianism, though he was only a strict vegetarian for eight or so years.

More convincingly, it was suggested that he probably didn't do himself much good by experimenting on himself with medicines and anaesthetics. Also, that he had simply worked too hard for too long – especially as he wasn't all that strong. He had had chest and kidney problems more than once, yet he had almost always worked long hours with little time off.

Whatever the reason, his family, friends and colleagues were shattered by his death.

He had just finished writing *On Chloroform and Other Anaesthetics* and had already asked Benjamin Richardson to write the introduction. Dr Richardson, as shaken and upset as the rest of John Snow's friends and family, wrote an obituary instead – a long obituary which grew into a biography and which appears at the beginning of the published book. In it, he explains that John Snow suffered a stroke (it was called apoplexy then). He seemed to recover from it – enough, anyway, to write the final chapter on chloroform, but then had a further stroke, and his body gave up on him.

After his death, a letter was published in *The Lancet*. It read:"Sir: I trust that the profession will evince some public testimony towards the late Dr John Snow. Who does not remember his frankness, his cordiality, his honesty, the absence of all disguise or affectation under an apparent off-hand manner. Her Majesty the Queen has been deprived of the future valuable services of a trustworthy, well-deserving, much-esteemed subject, by his sudden death. The poor have lost in him a real friend in the hour of need. W. Hooper Attree, Formerly House Surgeon to the Middlesex Hospital."

What can be seen in Broad Street now? Almost nothing Dr Snow would recognize. Just one section of the Georgian terraced houses, only slightly altered. The rest of the street has been rebuilt, some of it relatively recently, and it has even been renamed Broadwick Street.

There are other reminders, though.

A pub which stands on the corner of Broadwick Street and Lexington Street, and which used to be called 'The Newcastle upon Tyne', was renamed 'The John Snow' in 1956, the centenary of the publication of *On The Mode of Communication of Cholera*. (This would have surprised Dr Snow, if he could have known about it, because he disapproved of alcohol, although his friends managed to persuade him to 'take a little wine occasionally' for the sake of his health.)

And in 1992 Westminster City Council put up a model of the pump in Broadwick Street, symbolically minus its handle, "to mark a pioneering example of medical research in the service of public health". The original site of the pump is thought to have been outside the John Snow pub, but the pavement there is narrow so the council chose a more suitable site, a short way down on the other side of the road.

Dr Snow is buried in Brompton Cemetery, in London. Over his grave there stands quite a large memorial, which has been restored two or three times over the years. And beside it, under a small headstone, lies Charles Empson, his uncle, who died some years later but asked to be buried next to his nephew – whom perhaps he regarded as the son he never had.

John Snow is also commemorated in Dr Richardson's biography, which leaves a picture of a man who was a dedicated scientist and doctor, with a dry sense of humour, many friends, no pretensions and no greed for fame or money. A man who experimented on himself often and on animals only rarely, taking great care, if he did need to use an animal, to cause as little pain and distress as possible.

And he is remembered, too, in the writings of the Reverend Whitehead who quotes him as saying: "You and I may not live to see the day, and my name may be forgotten when it comes, but the time will arrive when great outbreaks of cholera will be things of the past; and it is the knowledge of the way in which the disease is propagated which will cause them to disappear."

The importance of Dr John Snow's contribution to

medicine was only really understood some time after his death. In fact, a great many things he would have found interesting happened after his death.

Louis Pasteur demonstrated that germs are borne of other germs, not spontaneously generated in rubbish and dirt.

The German bacteriologist Robert Koch identified the cholera germ itself, which made it possible to create a cholera vaccine.

Joseph Bazalgette rebuilt the entire sewerage system of London.

The stinking Thames was cleaned up, there was an end to cesspools, and constant mains water for all meant there was no longer any need to use the shallow wells.

Today, cholera is still a problem in some parts of the world – especially in the crowded and difficult conditions of refugee camps, but at least the crucial importance of rehydration is now known, and the facts that cholera lives on in the evacuations of patients and is water-borne. And that is the true legacy of this quiet, humorous, hard-working doctor.

Time Line for John Snow

1813   John Snow was born.

1827   Sent from home in York to Newcastle to be apprenticed to William Hardcastle.

1831   Cholera first reached Britain.

1833   Cholera had gone from Britain.

1836   John Snow walked from York to London.

1837   Snow enrolled in the Medical School of Westminster Hospital.

1838   Snow passed the qualifying exam of the Royal College of Surgeons, became a member of the Society of Apothecaries, and set up medical practice at 54 Frith Street.

1846   Snow first saw ether used as an anaesthetic and designed his own inhaler.

1848   Cholera flared up in Afghanistan and reached Britain again.

1849   Snow published the first version of his book, *On the Mode of Communication of Cholera*.

1853   Snow moved to 18 Sackville Street, and gave chloroform to Queen Victoria. The third epidemic of cholera hit London and Newcastle.

1854   The great outbreak of cholera in Soho.

1858   Snow completed *On Chloroform and Other Anaesthetics* just before he died.

Glossary

Abattoir: slaughterhouse.

Alimentary canal: the passage in the body through which food travels.

Anatomy: the study of the physical structure of animals, including humans.

Animacules: microscopic animals.

Apothecaries: chemists, pharmacists.

Apprentice/apprenticeship: a person taken on by a skilled person to learn a craft or trade.

Bacteria: micro-organisms, some of which cause disease.

Cesspool: underground chamber used to store sewage.

Clique: an exclusive group of people.

Consumption: tuberculosis, a disease of the lungs.

Dead-house: where bodies are laid out before burial.

Dehydration: excessive loss of water from the body.

Dissection: cutting up a body to study it.

Earthclosets: lavatories.

Foetid: [pronounced fetid] stinking.

Georgian: from the time of the British Kings George 1, 11, 111 and 1V (1714-1830).

Intravenous: into a vein.

Lightermen: men working on lighters – boats used to load and unload ships.

Miasma: [pronounced my-asma] foul vapours, unwholesome air.

Obituary: a death notice in a newspaper.

Omnivorous: eating all available foods.

Ozone: a form of oxygen present in the atmosphere.

Pestilence: a deadly epidemic disease.

Privies: lavatories.

Putrefaction: rottenness.

Rehydration: enabling a dehydrated person to absorb water.

Rookeries: crowded slums.

Sweatshop: a factory where workers work hard and earn little.

Toxins: poisons.

Trades union: an organised association of workers for the protection of their common interests.

Turncock: a person who turns the water supply on and off.

Watermen: boatmen, ferrymen.

Workhouse: an institution where the poor were housed in return for their labour.

Index